May you always celebr
the song in your hear
and share it with T
With deepest love, gratitude, + joy,
Weena Julapalli ♥

Dear Charlotte and Claire,
I hope this book brings
    you joy and encourages you
  to voice the songs in
    your hearts
        - Emma Lewis
  P.S. My dad is silly too

LISTEN TO THE SONG IN MY HEART

WRITTEN BY MEENA JULAPALLI

ILLUSTRATED BY EMMA LEWIS

Hardcover ISBN: 979-8-9876728-0-8
Paperback ISBN: 979-8-9876728-1-5
Ebook ISBN: 979-8-9876728-2-2

Library of Congress Control Number: 2023901921

Illustrations by: Emma Lewis

Printed in the U.S.A.

First Edition 2023
10 9 8 7 6 5 4 3 2 1

www.thejoyfulpath.org

TO THE ONE WHO MAKES MY HEART SING,
MY DEAR BEAUTIFUL MOTHER

ACROSS THE LANDS
AND BEYOND THE MOON

I HAVE MUSIC IN MY SOUL
AND IT PLAYS FOR YOU...

AS HIGH AS THE SKY,
AS DEEP AS THE OCEAN BLUE

I HAVE JOY IN MY SPIRIT
AND IT SHINES FOR YOU...

AS BRIGHTLY AS THE MIDDAY SUN,
AS SPARKLY AS THE MORNING DEW

I HAVE A SWING IN MY STEP
AND IT DANCES FOR YOU...

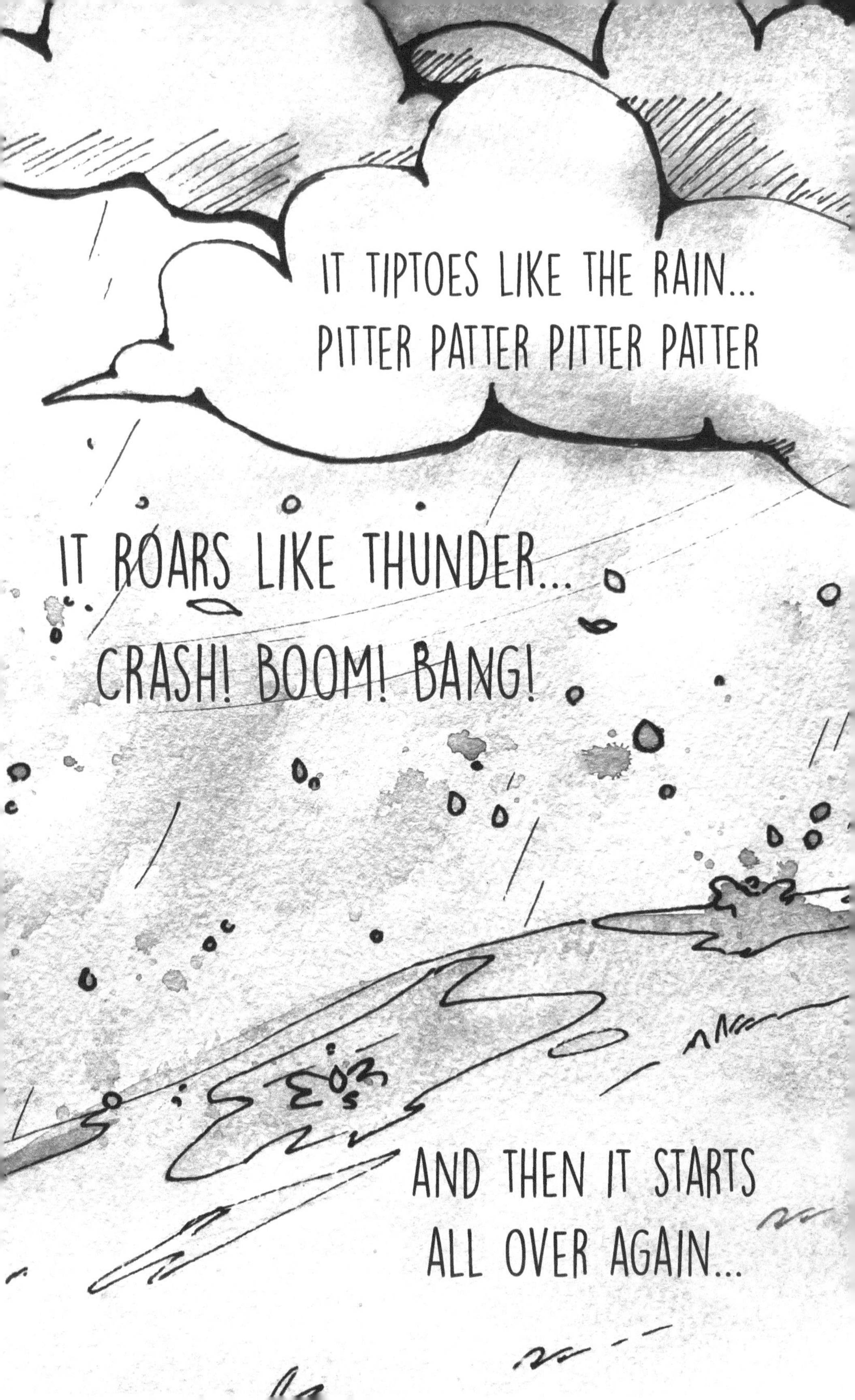
IT TIPTOES LIKE THE RAIN...
PITTER PATTER PITTER PATTER
IT ROARS LIKE THUNDER...
CRASH! BOOM! BANG!
AND THEN IT STARTS
ALL OVER AGAIN...

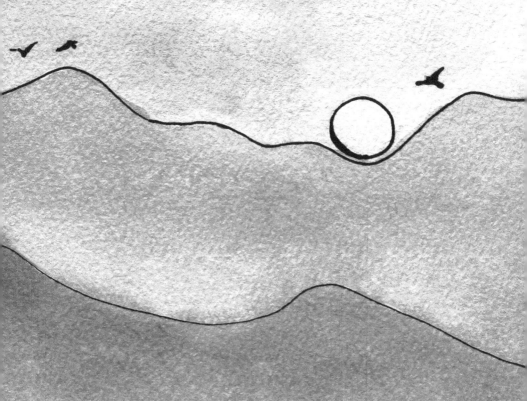

I HAVE A SONG IN MY HEART
AND IT LONGS TO BE FREE...

TO SHOW YOU HOW WONDERFUL
IT IS TO BE ME!

ACKNOWLEDGEMENTS

MY DEEPEST GRATITUDE TO MY PARENTS, SIBLINGS, AND FRIENDS
FOR THEIR SUPPORT AND ENCOURAGEMENT, TO KIMBERLY OEHRLEIN
FOR HER MAGICAL CRASH COURSE IN EDITING, AND TO THE LEWIS
FAMILY FOR GIVING ME THE OPPORTUNITY TO SHARE EMMA'S
BEAUTIFUL GIFT, THE SONG IN HER HEART, WITH THE WORLD.
EMMA, THANK YOU SO MUCH FOR BRINGING MY WORDS TO LIFE
WITH YOUR CREATIVE VISION AND FOR GIVING IT WINGS TO SOAR!
I AM SO PROUD OF YOU, AND I CAN'T WAIT TO SEE THE LIMITLESS
WAYS YOU WILL CONTINUE TO SHINE YOUR RADIANT LIGHT!

ABOUT THE AUTHOR

MEENA JULAPALLI, M.D., IS A BOARD—CERTIFIED PEDIATRIC DERMATOLOGIST IN HOUSTON, TEXAS AND A PROUD JOYOLOGIST IN THE SCHOOL OF LIFE. ONE WHOSE CALLING IS TO EMPOWER PEOPLE, PARTICULARLY CHILDREN, ALL AROUND THE WORLD TO DISCOVER, EXPERIENCE, CULTIVATE, EMBRACE, AND SHARE WHAT BRINGS THEM JOY. SHE IS THE FOUNDER OF THE JOYFUL PATH COOPERATIVE, WHOSE MISSION IS TO INSPIRE AND ENCOURAGE YOU TO SING YOUR OWN UNIQUE SONG. FOR MORE INFORMATION, VISIT WWW.THEJOYFULPATH.ORG

ABOUT THE ILLUSTRATOR

EMMA LEWIS IS A HIGH SCHOOL STUDENT LIVING IN SALT LAKE CITY, UTAH. SHE LOVES READING, PAINTING, AND TAKING CARE OF ANIMALS. AS A PERSON WITH HIGH—FUNCTIONING AUTISM, COMMUNICATION CAN BE DIFFICULT FOR HER; HOWEVER, SHE FEELS SHE CAN COMMUNICATE BEST THROUGH HER ARTISTIC EXPRESSION. SHE FINDS SOLACE IN PAINTING AND DRAWING. SHE ALSO USES THESE TALENTS TO HELP OTHERS AND RAISE MONEY FOR CHARITIES SUCH AS THE HUMANE SOCIETY.

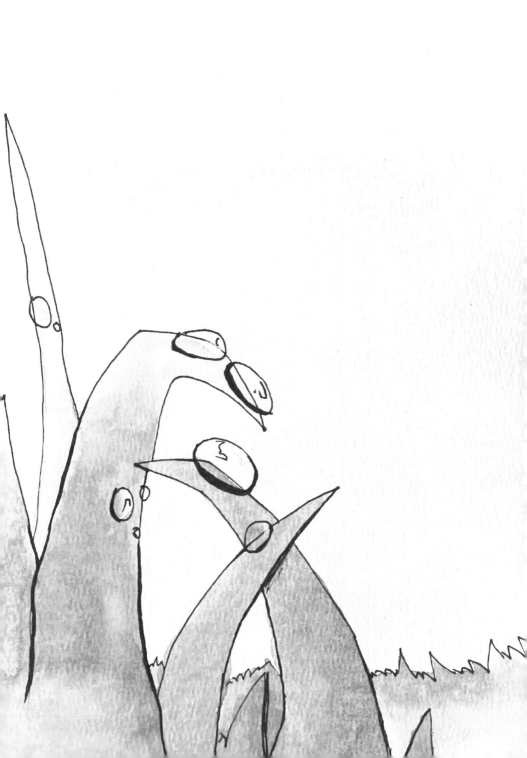

CPSIA information can be obtained
at www.ICGtesting.com
Printed in the USA
JSHW060346240223
38163JS00001B/1